First published 2003 by Egmont Books Ltd
239 Kensington High Street, London W8 6SA

© Disney. Based on the *Winnie-the-Pooh* works,
by A. A. Milne and E. H. Shepard

Colouring of the line illustrations from *Winnie-the-Pooh* and
The House at Pooh Corner copyright © 1970, 1973, 1974
Ernest H. Shepard and Egmont Books Ltd.

Colouring of the line illustrations from *When We Were Very Young*
and *Now We Are Six* by Mark Burgess
copyright © 1989 Egmont Books Ltd

3 5 7 9 10 8 6 4 2

Printed in China

ISBN 1 4052 0709 4

This address book uses the original illustrations by E. H. Shepard
and the text by A. A. Milne.

This book belongs to

_____

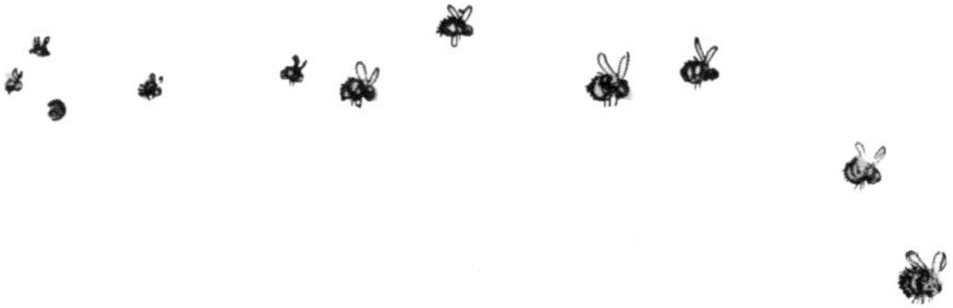

Winnie-the-Pooh

ADDRESS BOOK

A. A. Milne E. H. Shepard

Essential data for organised bears

Name _____

Address _____

_____

_____ Postcode _____

Telephone (home) _____

Telephone (work) _____

National Insurance number _____

Passport number _____

Driving Licence number _____

Car Registration _____

Breakdown Membership number _____

Car Insurance number _____

National Health number _____

Blood Group _____

Any Known Allergies _____

More numbers to remember

Dentist _____

Doctor _____

Cinema _____

Electrician _____

Gas _____

Insurance _____

Local Authority _____

Neighbour _____

Plumber _____

Police Station _____

Optician _____

Rail enquiries _____

Taxi _____

Telephone Engineer _____

Other _____

_____

_____

_____

"Do you know what this is?"

"No," said Piglet.

"It's an A."

"Oh," said Piglet.

"Not O – A," said Eeyore severely.

"Can't you HEAR, or do you think you have more education than Christopher Robin?"

A

name_____

address_____

_____ telephone_____

mobile_____ email_____

name_____

address_____

_____ telephone_____

mobile_____ email_____

name_____

address_____

_____ telephone_____

mobile_____ email_____

name_____

address_____

_____ telephone_____

mobile_____ email_____

name_____

address_____

_____ telephone_____

mobile_____ email_____

name_____
address_____
_____telephone_____
mobile_____email_____

name_____
address_____
_____telephone_____
mobile_____email_____

name_____
address_____
_____telephone_____
mobile_____email_____

name_____
address_____
_____telephone_____
mobile_____email_____

name_____
address_____
_____telephone_____
mobile_____email_____

name_____

address_____

_____telephone_____

mobile_____email_____

name_____

address_____

_____telephone_____

mobile_____email_____

name_____

address_____

_____telephone_____

mobile_____email_____

name_____

address_____

_____telephone_____

mobile_____email_____

name_____

address_____

_____telephone_____

mobile_____email_____

"Now then, Pooh," said Christopher Robin,
"where's your boat?"

"I ought to say," explained Pooh as they walked down
to the shore of the island, "that it isn't just an ordinary
sort of boat. Sometimes it's a Boat, and sometimes
it's more of an Accident. It all depends."

"Depends on what?"

"On whether I'm on the top of it or underneath it."

ℬ

name_____

address_____

_____telephone_____

mobile_____email_____

name_____

address_____

_____telephone_____

mobile_____email_____

name_____

address_____

_____telephone_____

mobile_____email_____

name_____

address_____

_____telephone_____

mobile_____email_____

name_____

address_____

_____telephone_____

mobile_____email_____

$\mathcal{B}$

name_____

address_____

_____telephone_____

mobile_____email_____

name_____

address_____

_____telephone_____

mobile_____email_____

name_____

address_____

_____telephone_____

mobile_____email_____

name_____

address_____

_____telephone_____

mobile_____email_____

name_____

address_____

_____telephone_____

mobile_____email_____

B

name_____

address_____

_____telephone_____

mobile_____email_____

name_____

address_____

_____telephone_____

mobile_____email_____

name_____

address_____

_____telephone_____

mobile_____email_____

name_____

address_____

_____telephone_____

mobile_____email_____

name_____

address_____

_____telephone_____

mobile_____email_____

"Well," said Owl, "the customary procedure in such cases is as follows."

"What does Crustimoney Proseedcake mean?" said Pooh. "For I am a Bear of Very Little Brain, and long words Bother me."

$\mathcal{C}$

name⎯⎯⎯⎯⎯⎯⎯⎯⎯⎯⎯⎯⎯⎯⎯⎯⎯⎯⎯⎯
address⎯⎯⎯⎯⎯⎯⎯⎯⎯⎯⎯⎯⎯⎯⎯⎯⎯⎯
⎯⎯⎯⎯⎯⎯⎯⎯⎯telephone⎯⎯⎯⎯⎯⎯
mobile⎯⎯⎯⎯⎯⎯⎯email⎯⎯⎯⎯⎯⎯

name⎯⎯⎯⎯⎯⎯⎯⎯⎯⎯⎯⎯⎯⎯⎯⎯⎯⎯⎯⎯
address⎯⎯⎯⎯⎯⎯⎯⎯⎯⎯⎯⎯⎯⎯⎯⎯⎯⎯
⎯⎯⎯⎯⎯⎯⎯⎯⎯telephone⎯⎯⎯⎯⎯⎯
mobile⎯⎯⎯⎯⎯⎯⎯email⎯⎯⎯⎯⎯⎯

name⎯⎯⎯⎯⎯⎯⎯⎯⎯⎯⎯⎯⎯⎯⎯⎯⎯⎯⎯⎯
address⎯⎯⎯⎯⎯⎯⎯⎯⎯⎯⎯⎯⎯⎯⎯⎯⎯⎯
⎯⎯⎯⎯⎯⎯⎯⎯⎯telephone⎯⎯⎯⎯⎯⎯
mobile⎯⎯⎯⎯⎯⎯⎯email⎯⎯⎯⎯⎯⎯

name⎯⎯⎯⎯⎯⎯⎯⎯⎯⎯⎯⎯⎯⎯⎯⎯⎯⎯⎯⎯
address⎯⎯⎯⎯⎯⎯⎯⎯⎯⎯⎯⎯⎯⎯⎯⎯⎯⎯
⎯⎯⎯⎯⎯⎯⎯⎯⎯telephone⎯⎯⎯⎯⎯⎯
mobile⎯⎯⎯⎯⎯⎯⎯email⎯⎯⎯⎯⎯⎯

name⎯⎯⎯⎯⎯⎯⎯⎯⎯⎯⎯⎯⎯⎯⎯⎯⎯⎯⎯⎯
address⎯⎯⎯⎯⎯⎯⎯⎯⎯⎯⎯⎯⎯⎯⎯⎯⎯⎯
⎯⎯⎯⎯⎯⎯⎯⎯⎯telephone⎯⎯⎯⎯⎯⎯
mobile⎯⎯⎯⎯⎯⎯⎯email⎯⎯⎯⎯⎯⎯

C

name_____
address_____
_____telephone_____
mobile_____email_____

name_____
address_____
_____telephone_____
mobile_____email_____

name_____
address_____
_____telephone_____
mobile_____email_____

name_____
address_____
_____telephone_____
mobile_____email_____

name_____
address_____
_____telephone_____
mobile_____email_____

name_____

address_____

_____telephone_____

mobile_____email_____

name_____

address_____

_____telephone_____

mobile_____email_____

name_____

address_____

_____telephone_____

mobile_____email_____

name_____

address_____

_____telephone_____

mobile_____email_____

name_____

address_____

_____telephone_____

mobile_____email_____

D

The Old Grey Donkey, Eeyore, stood by himself in a thistly corner of the Forest, his front feet well apart, his head on one side, and thought about things. Sometimes he thought sadly to himself, "Why?" and sometimes he thought, "Wherefore?" and sometimes he thought, "Inasmuch as which?" – and sometimes he didn't quite know what he WAS thinking about.

$\mathcal{D}$

name_____

address_____

_____telephone_____

mobile_____email_____

name_____

address_____

_____telephone_____

mobile_____email_____

name_____

address_____

_____telephone_____

mobile_____email_____

name_____

address_____

_____telephone_____

mobile_____email_____

name_____

address_____

_____telephone_____

mobile_____email_____

$\mathcal{D}$

name_____
address_____
_____telephone_____
mobile_____email_____

name_____
address_____
_____telephone_____
mobile_____email_____

name_____
address_____
_____telephone_____
mobile_____email_____

name_____
address_____
_____telephone_____
mobile_____email_____

name_____
address_____
_____telephone_____
mobile_____email_____

D

name⎯⎯⎯⎯⎯⎯⎯⎯⎯⎯⎯⎯⎯⎯⎯⎯⎯⎯⎯⎯⎯⎯⎯⎯
address⎯⎯⎯⎯⎯⎯⎯⎯⎯⎯⎯⎯⎯⎯⎯⎯⎯⎯⎯⎯⎯⎯
⎯⎯⎯⎯⎯⎯⎯⎯⎯⎯⎯telephone⎯⎯⎯⎯⎯⎯⎯⎯⎯
mobile⎯⎯⎯⎯⎯⎯⎯⎯email⎯⎯⎯⎯⎯⎯⎯⎯⎯⎯

name⎯⎯⎯⎯⎯⎯⎯⎯⎯⎯⎯⎯⎯⎯⎯⎯⎯⎯⎯⎯⎯⎯⎯⎯
address⎯⎯⎯⎯⎯⎯⎯⎯⎯⎯⎯⎯⎯⎯⎯⎯⎯⎯⎯⎯⎯⎯
⎯⎯⎯⎯⎯⎯⎯⎯⎯⎯⎯telephone⎯⎯⎯⎯⎯⎯⎯⎯⎯
mobile⎯⎯⎯⎯⎯⎯⎯⎯email⎯⎯⎯⎯⎯⎯⎯⎯⎯⎯

name⎯⎯⎯⎯⎯⎯⎯⎯⎯⎯⎯⎯⎯⎯⎯⎯⎯⎯⎯⎯⎯⎯⎯⎯
address⎯⎯⎯⎯⎯⎯⎯⎯⎯⎯⎯⎯⎯⎯⎯⎯⎯⎯⎯⎯⎯⎯
⎯⎯⎯⎯⎯⎯⎯⎯⎯⎯⎯telephone⎯⎯⎯⎯⎯⎯⎯⎯⎯
mobile⎯⎯⎯⎯⎯⎯⎯⎯email⎯⎯⎯⎯⎯⎯⎯⎯⎯⎯

name⎯⎯⎯⎯⎯⎯⎯⎯⎯⎯⎯⎯⎯⎯⎯⎯⎯⎯⎯⎯⎯⎯⎯⎯
address⎯⎯⎯⎯⎯⎯⎯⎯⎯⎯⎯⎯⎯⎯⎯⎯⎯⎯⎯⎯⎯⎯
⎯⎯⎯⎯⎯⎯⎯⎯⎯⎯⎯telephone⎯⎯⎯⎯⎯⎯⎯⎯⎯
mobile⎯⎯⎯⎯⎯⎯⎯⎯email⎯⎯⎯⎯⎯⎯⎯⎯⎯⎯

name⎯⎯⎯⎯⎯⎯⎯⎯⎯⎯⎯⎯⎯⎯⎯⎯⎯⎯⎯⎯⎯⎯⎯⎯
address⎯⎯⎯⎯⎯⎯⎯⎯⎯⎯⎯⎯⎯⎯⎯⎯⎯⎯⎯⎯⎯⎯
⎯⎯⎯⎯⎯⎯⎯⎯⎯⎯⎯telephone⎯⎯⎯⎯⎯⎯⎯⎯⎯
mobile⎯⎯⎯⎯⎯⎯⎯⎯email⎯⎯⎯⎯⎯⎯⎯⎯⎯⎯

"Thank you, Christopher Robin. You're the only one who seems to understand about tails. They don't think – that's what's the matter with some of these others. They've no imagination. A tail isn't a tail to THEM, it's just a Little Bit Extra at the back."

E

name_____

address_____

_____telephone_____

mobile_____email_____

name_____

address_____

_____telephone_____

mobile_____email_____

name_____

address_____

_____telephone_____

mobile_____email_____

name_____

address_____

_____telephone_____

mobile_____email_____

name_____

address_____

_____telephone_____

mobile_____email_____

name_____

address_____

_____telephone_____

mobile_____email_____

name_____

address_____

_____telephone_____

mobile_____email_____

name_____

address_____

_____telephone_____

mobile_____email_____

name_____

address_____

_____telephone_____

mobile_____email_____

name_____

address_____

_____telephone_____

mobile_____email_____

name_____
address_____
_____telephone_____
mobile_____email_____

name_____
address_____
_____telephone_____
mobile_____email_____

name_____
address_____
_____telephone_____
mobile_____email_____

name_____
address_____
_____telephone_____
mobile_____email_____

name_____
address_____
_____telephone_____
mobile_____email_____

... and when *Christopher Robin* had nailed it on in its right place again, *Eeyore* frisked about the forest, waving his tail so happily that *Winnie-the-Pooh* came over all funny, and had to hurry home for a little snack of something to sustain him.

$\mathcal{F}$

name_____
address_____
_____telephone_____
mobile_____email_____

name_____
address_____
_____telephone_____
mobile_____email_____

name_____
address_____
_____telephone_____
mobile_____email_____

name_____
address_____
_____telephone_____
mobile_____email_____

name_____
address_____
_____telephone_____
mobile_____email_____

F

name_____

address_____

_____telephone_____

mobile_____email_____

name_____

address_____

_____telephone_____

mobile_____email_____

name_____

address_____

_____telephone_____

mobile_____email_____

name_____

address_____

_____telephone_____

mobile_____email_____

name_____

address_____

_____telephone_____

mobile_____email_____

name_____

address_____

_____telephone_____

mobile_____email_____

name_____

address_____

_____telephone_____

mobile_____email_____

name_____

address_____

_____telephone_____

mobile_____email_____

name_____

address_____

_____telephone_____

mobile_____email_____

name_____

address_____

_____telephone_____

mobile_____email_____

"Good morning, Pooh Bear," said Eeyore gloomily. "If it IS a good morning," he said. "Which I doubt," said he.

"Why, what's the matter?"

"Nothing, Pooh Bear, nothing. We can't all, and some of us don't. That's all there is to it."

G

name_____

address_____

_____telephone_____

mobile_____email_____

name_____

address_____

_____telephone_____

mobile_____email_____

name_____

address_____

_____telephone_____

mobile_____email_____

name_____

address_____

_____telephone_____

mobile_____email_____

name_____

address_____

_____telephone_____

mobile_____email_____

G

name_____

address_____

_____ telephone_____

mobile_____ email_____

name_____

address_____

_____ telephone_____

mobile_____ email_____

name_____

address_____

_____ telephone_____

mobile_____ email_____

name_____

address_____

_____ telephone_____

mobile_____ email_____

name_____

address_____

_____ telephone_____

mobile_____ email_____

G

name_____

address_____

_____telephone_____

mobile_____email_____

name_____

address_____

_____telephone_____

mobile_____email_____

name_____

address_____

_____telephone_____

mobile_____email_____

name_____

address_____

_____telephone_____

mobile_____email_____

name_____

address_____

_____telephone_____

mobile_____email_____

Some hours later, just as the night was beginning to steal away, Pooh woke up suddenly with a sinking feeling. He had had that sinking feeling before, and he knew what it meant. *HE WAS HUNGRY.*

H

name_____

address_____

_____telephone_____

mobile_____email_____

name_____

address_____

_____telephone_____

mobile_____email_____

name_____

address_____

_____telephone_____

mobile_____email_____

name_____

address_____

_____telephone_____

mobile_____email_____

name_____

address_____

_____telephone_____

mobile_____email_____

$\mathcal{H}$

name_____

address_____

_____telephone_____

mobile_____email_____

name_____

address_____

_____telephone_____

mobile_____email_____

name_____

address_____

_____telephone_____

mobile_____email_____

name_____

address_____

_____telephone_____

mobile_____email_____

name_____

address_____

_____telephone_____

mobile_____email_____

name_____

address_____

_____telephone_____

mobile_____email_____

name_____

address_____

_____telephone_____

mobile_____email_____

name_____

address_____

_____telephone_____

mobile_____email_____

name_____

address_____

_____telephone_____

mobile_____email_____

name_____

address_____

_____telephone_____

mobile_____email_____

"There is an Invitation for you."
"What's that like?"
"An Invitation!"
"Yes, I heard you. Who dropped it?"

J

name_____

address_____

_____telephone_____

mobile_____email_____

name_____

address_____

_____telephone_____

mobile_____email_____

name_____

address_____

_____telephone_____

mobile_____email_____

name_____

address_____

_____telephone_____

mobile_____email_____

name_____

address_____

_____telephone_____

mobile_____email_____

name_____

address_____

_____telephone_____

mobile_____email_____

name_____

address_____

_____telephone_____

mobile_____email_____

name_____

address_____

_____telephone_____

mobile_____email_____

name_____

address_____

_____telephone_____

mobile_____email_____

name_____

address_____

_____telephone_____

mobile_____email_____

name_____
address_____
_____telephone_____
mobile_____email_____

name_____
address_____
_____telephone_____
mobile_____email_____

name_____
address_____
_____telephone_____
mobile_____email_____

name_____
address_____
_____telephone_____
mobile_____email_____

name_____
address_____
_____telephone_____
mobile_____email_____

"Is it One of the Fiercer Animals?"
he said, looking the other way.
Pooh nodded. "It's a Jagular," he said.
"What do Jagulars do?" asked
Piglet, hoping that they wouldn't.

name_____

address_____

_____ telephone_____

mobile_____ email_____

name_____

address_____

_____ telephone_____

mobile_____ email_____

name_____

address_____

_____ telephone_____

mobile_____ email_____

name_____

address_____

_____ telephone_____

mobile_____ email_____

name_____

address_____

_____ telephone_____

mobile_____ email_____

name_____

address_____

_____telephone_____

mobile_____email_____

name_____

address_____

_____telephone_____

mobile_____email_____

name_____

address_____

_____telephone_____

mobile_____email_____

name_____

address_____

_____telephone_____

mobile_____email_____

name_____

address_____

_____telephone_____

mobile_____email_____

name_____

address_____

_____telephone_____

mobile_____email_____

name_____

address_____

_____telephone_____

mobile_____email_____

name_____

address_____

_____telephone_____

mobile_____email_____

name_____

address_____

_____telephone_____

mobile_____email_____

name_____

address_____

_____telephone_____

mobile_____email_____

"Is it a very Grand thing to be an
Afternoon, what you said?"
"A what?" said Christopher Robin
lazily, as he listened to something else.
"On a horse?" explained Pooh.
"A Knight?"
"Oh, was that it?" said Pooh.

K

name_____

address_____

_____telephone_____

mobile_____email_____

name_____

address_____

_____telephone_____

mobile_____email_____

name_____

address_____

_____telephone_____

mobile_____email_____

name_____

address_____

_____telephone_____

mobile_____email_____

name_____

address_____

_____telephone_____

mobile_____email_____

K

name

address

telephone

mobile _____ email

name

address

telephone

mobile _____ email

name

address

telephone

mobile _____ email

name

address

telephone

mobile _____ email

name

address

telephone

mobile _____ email

_K_

name _____

address _____

_____ telephone _____

mobile _____ email _____

name _____

address _____

_____ telephone _____

mobile _____ email _____

name _____

address _____

_____ telephone _____

mobile _____ email _____

name _____

address _____

_____ telephone _____

mobile _____ email _____

name _____

address _____

_____ telephone _____

mobile _____ email _____

"Oh, Bear!" said
Christopher Robin.
"How I do love you!"
"So do I," said Pooh.

L

name_____

address_____

_____telephone_____

mobile_____email_____

name_____

address_____

_____telephone_____

mobile_____email_____

name_____

address_____

_____telephone_____

mobile_____email_____

name_____

address_____

_____telephone_____

mobile_____email_____

name_____

address_____

_____telephone_____

mobile_____email_____

name_____

address_____

_____telephone_____

mobile_____email_____

name_____

address_____

_____telephone_____

mobile_____email_____

name_____

address_____

_____telephone_____

mobile_____email_____

name_____

address_____

_____telephone_____

mobile_____email_____

name_____

address_____

_____telephone_____

mobile_____email_____

name_____

address_____

_____telephone_____

mobile_____email_____

name_____

address_____

_____telephone_____

mobile_____email_____

name_____

address_____

_____telephone_____

mobile_____email_____

name_____

address_____

_____telephone_____

mobile_____email_____

name_____

address_____

_____telephone_____

mobile_____email_____

$\mathcal{M}$

"It's a Missage," he said to himself, "that's what it is. And that letter is a 'P', and so is that, and so is that, and 'P' means 'Pooh', so it's a very important Missage to me, and I can't read it. I must find Christopher Robin or Owl or Piglet, one of those Clever Readers who can read things, and they will tell me what this missage means ..."

M

name_____

address_____

_____ telephone_____

mobile_____ email_____

name_____

address_____

_____ telephone_____

mobile_____ email_____

name_____

address_____

_____ telephone_____

mobile_____ email_____

name_____

address_____

_____ telephone_____

mobile_____ email_____

name_____

address_____

_____ telephone_____

mobile_____ email_____

M

name_____

address_____

_____ telephone _____

mobile_____ email _____

name_____

address_____

_____ telephone _____

mobile_____ email _____

name_____

address_____

_____ telephone _____

mobile_____ email _____

name_____

address_____

_____ telephone _____

mobile_____ email _____

name_____

address_____

_____ telephone _____

mobile_____ email _____

name_____

address_____

_____telephone_____

mobile_____email_____

name_____

address_____

_____telephone_____

mobile_____email_____

name_____

address_____

_____telephone_____

mobile_____email_____

name_____

address_____

_____telephone_____

mobile_____email_____

name_____

address_____

_____telephone_____

mobile_____email_____

"How do you do Nothing?" asked Pooh, after he had wondered for a long time.

"Well, it's when people call out at you just as you're going off to do it, 'What are you going to do, Christopher Robin?' and you say 'Oh, nothing,' and then you go and do it."

"Oh, I see," said Pooh.

name_____

address_____

_____ telephone_____

mobile_____ email_____

name_____

address_____

_____ telephone_____

mobile_____ email_____

name_____

address_____

_____ telephone_____

mobile_____ email_____

name_____

address_____

_____ telephone_____

mobile_____ email_____

name_____

address_____

_____ telephone_____

mobile_____ email_____

N

name_____

address_____

_____ telephone_____

mobile_____ email_____

name_____

address_____

_____ telephone_____

mobile_____ email_____

name_____

address_____

_____ telephone_____

mobile_____ email_____

name_____

address_____

_____ telephone_____

mobile_____ email_____

name_____

address_____

_____ telephone_____

mobile_____ email_____

name_____
address_____
_____
_____telephone_____
mobile_____email_____

name_____
address_____
_____
_____telephone_____
mobile_____email_____

name_____
address_____
_____
_____telephone_____
mobile_____email_____

name_____
address_____
_____
_____telephone_____
mobile_____email_____

name_____
address_____
_____
_____telephone_____
mobile_____email_____

O

"That's right. You'll like Owl. He flew past a day or two ago and noticed me. He didn't actually say anything, mind you, but he knew it was me. Very friendly of him, I thought. Encouraging."

name_____

address_____

_____telephone_____

mobile_____email_____

name_____

address_____

_____telephone_____

mobile_____email_____

name_____

address_____

_____telephone_____

mobile_____email_____

name_____

address_____

_____telephone_____

mobile_____email_____

name_____

address_____

_____telephone_____

mobile_____email_____

name_____
address_____
_____telephone_____
mobile_____email_____

name_____
address_____
_____telephone_____
mobile_____email_____

name_____
address_____
_____telephone_____
mobile_____email_____

name_____
address_____
_____telephone_____
mobile_____email_____

name_____
address_____
_____telephone_____
mobile_____email_____

name_____
address_____
_____telephone_____
mobile_____email_____

name_____
address_____
_____telephone_____
mobile_____email_____

name_____
address_____
_____telephone_____
mobile_____email_____

name_____
address_____
_____telephone_____
mobile_____email_____

name_____
address_____
_____telephone_____
mobile_____email_____

P

"… And we must all bring Provisions."
"Bring what?"
"Things to eat."

$\mathcal{P}$

name_____

address_____

_____telephone_____

mobile_____email_____

name_____

address_____

_____telephone_____

mobile_____email_____

name_____

address_____

_____telephone_____

mobile_____email_____

name_____

address_____

_____telephone_____

mobile_____email_____

name_____

address_____

_____telephone_____

mobile_____email_____

name_____

address_____

_____telephone_____

mobile_____email_____

name_____

address_____

_____telephone_____

mobile_____email_____

name_____

address_____

_____telephone_____

mobile_____email_____

name_____

address_____

_____telephone_____

mobile_____email_____

name_____

address_____

_____telephone_____

mobile_____email_____

name_____

address_____

_____telephone_____

mobile_____email_____

name_____

address_____

_____telephone_____

mobile_____email_____

name_____

address_____

_____telephone_____

mobile_____email_____

name_____

address_____

_____telephone_____

mobile_____email_____

name_____

address_____

_____telephone_____

mobile_____email_____

... *Tigger, who had been hiding behind trees and jumping out on Pooh's shadow when it wasn't looking, said that Tiggers were only bouncy before breakfast, and that as soon as they had had a few haycorns they became Quiet and Refined.*

Q

name_____

address_____

_____ telephone_____

mobile_____ email_____

name_____

address_____

_____ telephone_____

mobile_____ email_____

name_____

address_____

_____ telephone_____

mobile_____ email_____

name_____

address_____

_____ telephone_____

mobile_____ email_____

name_____

address_____

_____ telephone_____

mobile_____ email_____

name_____
address_____
_____telephone_____
mobile_____email_____

name_____
address_____
_____telephone_____
mobile_____email_____

name_____
address_____
_____telephone_____
mobile_____email_____

name_____
address_____
_____telephone_____
mobile_____email_____

name_____
address_____
_____telephone_____
mobile_____email_____

name_____
address_____
_____telephone_____
mobile_____email_____

name_____
address_____
_____telephone_____
mobile_____email_____

name_____
address_____
_____telephone_____
mobile_____email_____

name_____
address_____
_____telephone_____
mobile_____email_____

name_____
address_____
_____telephone_____
mobile_____email_____

R

"Who is Small?"
"One of my friends-and-relations," said Rabbit carelessly.
This didn't help Pooh much, because Rabbit had so many friends-and-relations, and of such different sorts and sizes, that he didn't know whether he ought to be looking for Small at the top of an oak-tree or in the petal of a buttercup.

R

name_____

address_____

_____telephone_____

mobile_____email_____

name_____

address_____

_____telephone_____

mobile_____email_____

name_____

address_____

_____telephone_____

mobile_____email_____

name_____

address_____

_____telephone_____

mobile_____email_____

name_____

address_____

_____telephone_____

mobile_____email_____

$\mathcal{R}$

name_____
address_____
_____telephone_____
mobile_____email_____

name_____
address_____
_____telephone_____
mobile_____email_____

name_____
address_____
_____telephone_____
mobile_____email_____

name_____
address_____
_____telephone_____
mobile_____email_____

name_____
address_____
_____telephone_____
mobile_____email_____

name_____

address_____

_____telephone_____

mobile_____email_____

name_____

address_____

_____telephone_____

mobile_____email_____

name_____

address_____

_____telephone_____

mobile_____email_____

name_____

address_____

_____telephone_____

mobile_____email_____

name_____

address_____

_____telephone_____

mobile_____email_____

"If anybody wants to clap," said Eeyore ...
"now is the time to do it."
They all clapped.
"Thank you," said Eeyore. "Unexpected
and gratifying, if a little lacking in Smack."

name_____

address_____

_____telephone_____

mobile_____email_____

name_____

address_____

_____telephone_____

mobile_____email_____

name_____

address_____

_____telephone_____

mobile_____email_____

name_____

address_____

_____telephone_____

mobile_____email_____

name_____

address_____

_____telephone_____

mobile_____email_____

name_____

address_____

_____ telephone_____

mobile_____ email_____

name_____

address_____

_____ telephone_____

mobile_____ email_____

name_____

address_____

_____ telephone_____

mobile_____ email_____

name_____

address_____

_____ telephone_____

mobile_____ email_____

name_____

address_____

_____ telephone_____

mobile_____ email_____

name_____
address_____
_____telephone_____
mobile_____email_____

name_____
address_____
_____telephone_____
mobile_____email_____

name_____
address_____
_____telephone_____
mobile_____email_____

name_____
address_____
_____telephone_____
mobile_____email_____

name_____
address_____
_____telephone_____
mobile_____email_____

Half-way between Pooh's house and Piglet's house was a Thoughtful Spot where they met sometimes when they had decided to go and see each other, and as it was warm and out of the wind they would sit down there for a little and wonder what they would do now that they HAD seen each other.

name_____

address_____

_____telephone_____

mobile_____email_____

name_____

address_____

_____telephone_____

mobile_____email_____

name_____

address_____

_____telephone_____

mobile_____email_____

name_____

address_____

_____telephone_____

mobile_____email_____

name_____

address_____

_____telephone_____

mobile_____email_____

name_____

address_____

_____telephone_____

mobile_____email_____

name_____

address_____

_____telephone_____

mobile_____email_____

name_____

address_____

_____telephone_____

mobile_____email_____

name_____

address_____

_____telephone_____

mobile_____email_____

name_____

address_____

_____telephone_____

mobile_____email_____

name_____

address_____

_____ telephone_____

mobile_____ email_____

name_____

address_____

_____ telephone_____

mobile_____ email_____

name_____

address_____

_____ telephone_____

mobile_____ email_____

name_____

address_____

_____ telephone_____

mobile_____ email_____

name_____

address_____

_____ telephone_____

mobile_____ email_____

U

"It's Piglet!" cried Pooh eagerly.
"Where are you?"
"Underneath," said Piglet
in an underneath sort of way.
"Underneath what?"
"You," squeaked Piglet. "Get up!"

U

name_____

address_____

_____telephone_____

mobile_____email_____

name_____

address_____

_____telephone_____

mobile_____email_____

name_____

address_____

_____telephone_____

mobile_____email_____

name_____

address_____

_____telephone_____

mobile_____email_____

name_____

address_____

_____telephone_____

mobile_____email_____

U

name_____
address_____
_____telephone_____
mobile_____email_____

name_____
address_____
_____telephone_____
mobile_____email_____

name_____
address_____
_____telephone_____
mobile_____email_____

name_____
address_____
_____telephone_____
mobile_____email_____

name_____
address_____
_____telephone_____
mobile_____email_____

name_____

address_____

_____telephone_____

mobile_____email_____

name_____

address_____

_____telephone_____

mobile_____email_____

name_____

address_____

_____telephone_____

mobile_____email_____

name_____

address_____

_____telephone_____

mobile_____email_____

name_____

address_____

_____telephone_____

mobile_____email_____

V

WHERE SHOULD THEY DIG
THE VERY DEEP PIT?
Piglet said that the best place
would be somewhere where
a Heffalump was, just before
he fell into it, only about a foot
further on.

V

name_____

address_____

_____ telephone_____

mobile_____ email_____

name_____

address_____

_____ telephone_____

mobile_____ email_____

name_____

address_____

_____ telephone_____

mobile_____ email_____

name_____

address_____

_____ telephone_____

mobile_____ email_____

name_____

address_____

_____ telephone_____

mobile_____ email_____

name_____
address_____
_____telephone_____
mobile_____email_____

name_____
address_____
_____telephone_____
mobile_____email_____

name_____
address_____
_____telephone_____
mobile_____email_____

name_____
address_____
_____telephone_____
mobile_____email_____

name_____
address_____
_____telephone_____
mobile_____email_____

name_____

address_____

_____ telephone_____

mobile_____ email_____

name_____

address_____

_____ telephone_____

mobile_____ email_____

name_____

address_____

_____ telephone_____

mobile_____ email_____

name_____

address_____

_____ telephone_____

mobile_____ email_____

name_____

address_____

_____ telephone_____

mobile_____ email_____

*He could spell his own name WOL,
and he could spell Tuesday so that you
knew it wasn't Wednesday, and he
could read quite comfortably when you
weren't looking over his shoulder and
saying "Well?" all the time …*

W
X

name

address

                       telephone

mobile   email

name

address

                       telephone

mobile   email

name

address

                       telephone

mobile   email

name

address

                       telephone

mobile   email

name

address

                       telephone

mobile   email

𝒲

name_____
address_____
_____telephone_____
mobile_____email_____

name_____
address_____
_____telephone_____
mobile_____email_____

name_____
address_____
_____telephone_____
mobile_____email_____

name_____
address_____
_____telephone_____
mobile_____email_____

name_____
address_____
_____telephone_____
mobile_____email_____

name_____

address_____

_____telephone_____

mobile_____email_____

name_____

address_____

_____telephone_____

mobile_____email_____

name_____

address_____

_____telephone_____

mobile_____email_____

name_____

address_____

_____telephone_____

mobile_____email_____

name_____

address_____

_____telephone_____

mobile_____email_____

"We are all going on an Expedition," said
Christopher Robin, as he got up and brushed himself.
"Thank you, Pooh."
"Going on an Expotition?" said Pooh eagerly.
"I don't think I've ever been on one of those.
Where are we going to on this Expotition?"
"Expedition, silly old Bear. It's got an 'x' in it."

name_____

address_____

_____telephone_____

mobile_____email_____

name_____

address_____

_____telephone_____

mobile_____email_____

name_____

address_____

_____telephone_____

mobile_____email_____

name_____

address_____

_____telephone_____

mobile_____email_____

name_____

address_____

_____telephone_____

mobile_____email_____

name_____
address_____
_____telephone_____
mobile_____email_____

name_____
address_____
_____telephone_____
mobile_____email_____

name_____
address_____
_____telephone_____
mobile_____email_____

name_____
address_____
_____telephone_____
mobile_____email_____

name_____
address_____
_____telephone_____
mobile_____email_____

name_____

address_____

_____telephone_____

mobile_____email_____

name_____

address_____

_____telephone_____

mobile_____email_____

name_____

address_____

_____telephone_____

mobile_____email_____

name_____

address_____

_____telephone_____

mobile_____email_____

name_____

address_____

_____telephone_____

mobile_____email_____

"I might have known," said Eeyore. "After all, one can't complain. I have my friends. Somebody spoke to me only yesterday. And was it last week or the week before that Rabbit bumped into me and said 'Bother!' The Social Round. Always something going on."

Y

name _____

address _____

_____ telephone _____

mobile _____ email _____

name _____

address _____

_____ telephone _____

mobile _____ email _____

name _____

address _____

_____ telephone _____

mobile _____ email _____

name _____

address _____

_____ telephone _____

mobile _____ email _____

name _____

address _____

_____ telephone _____

mobile _____ email _____

Y

name_____

address_____

_____telephone_____

mobile_____email_____

name_____

address_____

_____telephone_____

mobile_____email_____

name_____

address_____

_____telephone_____

mobile_____email_____

name_____

address_____

_____telephone_____

mobile_____email_____

name_____

address_____

_____telephone_____

mobile_____email_____

Y

name _____

address _____

_____ telephone _____

mobile _____ email _____

name _____

address _____

_____ telephone _____

mobile _____ email _____

name _____

address _____

_____ telephone _____

mobile _____ email _____

name _____

address _____

_____ telephone _____

mobile _____ email _____

name _____

address _____

_____ telephone _____

mobile _____ email _____

"*That buzzing-noise means something.
You don't get a buzzing-noise like
that, just buzzing and buzzing,
without its meaning something. If
there's a buzzing-noise, somebody's
making a buzzing-noise, and the only
reason for making a buzzing-noise that
I know of is because you're a bee …*

*… And the only reason for being a bee
that I know of is making honey …*"

Z

name_____

address_____

_____telephone_____

mobile_____email_____

name_____

address_____

_____telephone_____

mobile_____email_____

name_____

address_____

_____telephone_____

mobile_____email_____

name_____

address_____

_____telephone_____

mobile_____email_____

name_____

address_____

_____telephone_____

mobile_____email_____

name_____
address_____
_____telephone_____
mobile_____email_____

name_____
address_____
_____telephone_____
mobile_____email_____

name_____
address_____
_____telephone_____
mobile_____email_____

name_____
address_____
_____telephone_____
mobile_____email_____

name_____
address_____
_____telephone_____
mobile_____email_____

Z

name _____

address _____

_____ telephone _____

mobile _____ email _____

name _____

address _____

_____ telephone _____

mobile _____ email _____

name _____

address _____

_____ telephone _____

mobile _____ email _____

name _____

address _____

_____ telephone _____

mobile _____ email _____

name _____

address _____

_____ telephone _____

mobile _____ email _____

name

address

telephone

mobile   email

name

address

telephone

mobile   email

name

address

telephone

mobile   email

name

address

telephone

mobile   email

name

address

telephone

mobile   email

More friends-and-relations

name_____

address_____

_____telephone_____

mobile_____email_____

name_____

address_____

_____telephone_____

mobile_____email_____

name_____

address_____

_____telephone_____

mobile_____email_____

name_____

address_____

_____telephone_____

mobile_____email_____

name_____

address_____

_____telephone_____

mobile_____email_____

More friends-and-relations

name _____

address _____

_____ telephone _____

mobile _____ email _____

name _____

address _____

_____ telephone _____

mobile _____ email _____

name _____

address _____

_____ telephone _____

mobile _____ email _____

name _____

address _____

_____ telephone _____

mobile _____ email _____

name _____

address _____

_____ telephone _____

mobile _____ email _____

More friends-and-relations

name_____

address_____

_____ telephone_____

mobile_____ email_____

name_____

address_____

_____ telephone_____

mobile_____ email_____

name_____

address_____

_____ telephone_____

mobile_____ email_____

name_____

address_____

_____ telephone_____

mobile_____ email_____

More friends-and-relations

name_____
address_____
_____telephone_____
mobile_____email_____

name_____
address_____
_____telephone_____
mobile_____email_____

name_____
address_____
_____telephone_____
mobile_____email_____

name_____
address_____
_____telephone_____
mobile_____email_____

name_____
address_____
_____telephone_____
mobile_____email_____

More friends-and-relations

name_____

address_____

_____telephone_____

mobile_____email_____

name_____

address_____

_____telephone_____

mobile_____email_____

name_____

address_____

_____telephone_____

mobile_____email_____

name_____

address_____

_____telephone_____

mobile_____email_____

name_____

address_____

_____telephone_____

mobile_____email_____

More friends-and-relations

name_____

address_____

_____ telephone_____

mobile_____ email_____

name_____

address_____

_____ telephone_____

mobile_____ email_____

name_____

address_____

_____ telephone_____

mobile_____ email_____

name_____

address_____

_____ telephone_____

mobile_____ email_____

name_____

address_____

_____ telephone_____

mobile_____ email_____

Birthdays

name _____

birthday _____

name _____

birthday _____

name _____

birthday _____

name _____

birthday _____

name _____

birthday _____

name _____

birthday _____

Birthdays

name _____

birthday _____

name _____

birthday _____

name _____

birthday _____

name _____

birthday _____

name _____

birthday _____

name _____

birthday _____

name _____

birthday _____

name _____

birthday _____

name _____

birthday _____

name _____

birthday _____

Birthdays

name _____

birthday _____

name _____

birthday _____

name _____

birthday _____

name _____

birthday _____

name _____

birthday _____

name _____

birthday _____

name _____

birthday _____

name _____

birthday _____

name _____

birthday _____

name _____

birthday _____

Birthdays

name _____

birthday _____

name _____

birthday _____

name _____

birthday _____

name _____

birthday _____

name _____

birthday _____

name _____

birthday _____

name _____

birthday _____

name _____

birthday _____

name _____

birthday _____

name _____

birthday _____